YOUR FAITH / YOUR COMMITMENT / GOD'S CALL

confirm

STUDENT GUIDE

APPROVED UNITED METHODIST CONFIRMATION

Confirm Student Guide
Your Faith. Your Commitment. God's Call.

Contents

Lesson 1: Traveling Together

— E X P L O R E —

Moses: Exodus 3:1-14; 4:1-5, 10-16
Samuel: 1 Samuel 3:1-19

— R E F L E C T —

Be honest: How are you feeling about beginning confirmation?
Write down three different emotions that you are feeling.

Who from the Bible can you think of who experienced similar
emotions before setting out on a journey with God?

List 3 people you can talk to about your experiences and
feelings during your confirmation journey.

— C R E A T E —

Dear Future Me

Use the space on the next page to write a letter to the future
version of yourself who has completed your confirmation
journey. Include how you are feeling as you begin this journey
and how you are hoping to grow along the way. What images or
words describe what you are anticipating on your confirmation
journey? When you finish writing your letter, tape page 5 closed
and leave it sealed until your last confirmation class.

Visas

VIST
VAL
CHIC
LIRE
P. N.

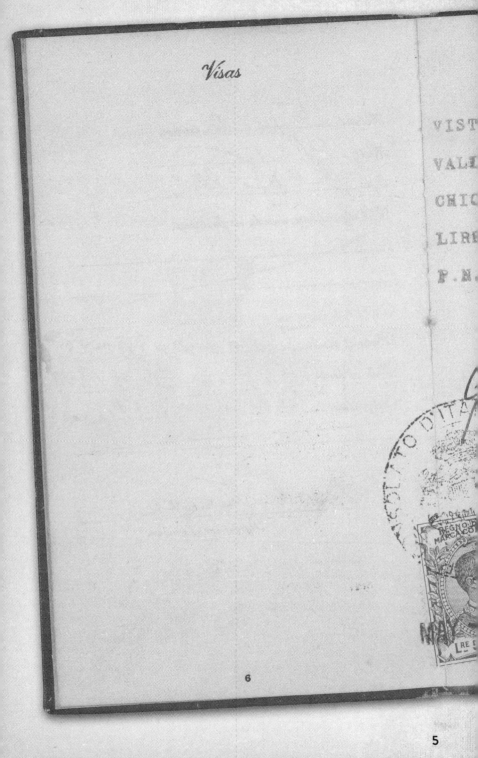

6

Fold along dotted line and tape closed until your last confirmation class.

— N E X T —

Ideas to Try This Week

At home: Find some old family photos of your parents when they were your age. What emotions do you think your parents felt when they were younger? Show them your favorite photo and ask them about their life and faith when they were your age.

At school: Ask a friend to tell you about the last trip he or she took. Ask what he or she did to prepare for the journey and what the experience was like along the way. How does your friend's story relate to the confirmation journey you are beginning? What can you learn from your friend's experience?

In your community: Take a prayer walk around your neighborhood, remembering that God is with you every step of the way. Pause at least three times on your walk and say this prayer: "God, you are with me every step of the way. Continue to guide my faith as I enter my confirmation journey."

— M Y I D E A S —

— R E A D M O R E —

More about Moses' birth—Exodus 2:1-14
More about Samuel's birth—1 Samuel 1:3-20
Beginning of King David's journey—1 Samuel 16:1-13
Beginning of the Disciples' journey—Matthew 10:1-15

Lesson 2: Living Together

— EXPLORE —

Ecclesiastes 4:9-12; Jeremiah 31:31-34
Romans 8:37-39; Colossians 3:12-17

— REFLECT —

The United Methodist Book of Discipline (paragraph 217)
Reflect on this list from the *Book of Discipline.* Circle words and phrases that you are drawn to. Underline words and phrases that you don't understand.

They covenant together with God and with members of the local church to keep the vows which are a part of the order of confirmation and reception into the church:

To renounce the spiritual forces of wickedness, reject the evil powers of the world, and repent of their sin;

To accept the freedom and power God gives them to resist evil, injustice, and oppression;

To confess Jesus Christ as Savior, put their whole trust in his grace, and promise to serve him as their Lord;

To remain faithful members of Christ's holy church and serve as Christ's representatives in the world;

To be loyal to Christ through The United Methodist Church and do all in their power to strengthen its ministries;

To faithfully participate in its ministries by their prayers, their presence, their gifts, their service, and their witness;

To receive and profess the Christian faith as contained in the Scriptures of the Old and New Testaments

— CREATE —

Confirmation, Community, and Covenant

You will be brainstorming these elements together as a group: first on sticky notes, then adding your favorites here.

Prayers: whom and what our group will pray for during this journey:

Presence: ways we can be fully present in our local church:

Gifts: ways we can financially support the work of the church here and all over the world:

Service: ways we could serve the church during our confirmation journey:

Witness: ways our group could show and tell others about our faith:

— N E X T —

Ideas to Try This Week
At home: Talk with your family about the norms and expectations you share. Whether it's official or unofficial, what is your family covenant? Lead your family through some of the questions you discussed in this confirmation lesson and create a family covenant together.

At school: Think about a time when you felt like you belonged at school, either your current school or another school you went to. What about that time made you feel connected? Who helped you to feel like you were part of something more than yourself? What could you do to help others feel a sense of belonging at school this week?

In your community: Introduce yourself to your neighbors. Whether you know them or not, knock on their door and say hello. Ask them what it means for them to be a part of the community. And then tell them what it means for you! (Hint: If your family does not know the people who live around you, be sure to talk to your parents or guardians before you knock on a strangers' door. You might want to bring an adult along.)

— M Y   I D E A S —

— R E A D   M O R E —

God's covenant with Abraham—Genesis 17:1-8
Early Christian community—Acts 4:32-35
Christian accountability—Galatians 6:1-5
Welcoming one another like Christ—Romans 14:1-12

Lesson 3: Loving Together

— EXPLORE —

John 13:34-35 and 15:9-17

— REFLECT —

Showing Love

List 3 people who've shown you that they love you and how they express their love:

List 3 ways this confirmation group could show that we love one another:

List 3 ways you can show someone you don't know that you love him or her.

— CREATE —

'Show Love to Others' Day

With a partner, fill in the blanks below with words or pictures to imagine a love-filled day.

You wake up in the morning after hitting snooze on your alarm — twice. You get ready as fast as you can to avoid being late for school. You stop to look at yourself in the mirror. Today will be filled with loving others, but you first pause to sense God's love. What do you do or say?

You dash into the kitchen to grab something to eat. Your family is there already. Apparently, they didn't hit snooze as much as you did. They all look up as you enter the room. Remembering that this is your day to show some love, what do you say to them?

You arrive at school with only minutes to spare, half-walking, half-running to get to your science class. Two of your friends are already sitting at your table. When you join them, what do you say and do to show some love?

It turns out that your favorite teacher is out sick today. And if that's not bad enough, your least favorite substitute is filling in. You can think of many ways you want to respond to this news, but most of them aren't filled with love. Instead, what do you say or do?

It's time for lunch. You walk into the lunchroom and see so many different people, some of them sitting with friends and others sitting alone. Where do you sit, and what do you say to show some genuine love?

The school day is finally over. You and your friends have the rest of the day free. They look to you for a suggestion of what you should all do together. This is your chance to make this day even better. What do you do with your friends to show love to others?

You're back at home after an amazing love-filled day. You're about to go to bed and get ready for another one, but first you pause to say a prayer to God. What do you pray?

— NEXT —

Ideas to Try This Week

At home: Think of one thing you can do to show love to everyone in your immediate family. Do at least one of them each day this week.

At school: Revisit one scene from the love-filled day you created. Be intentional about bringing this scene to life. Afterwards take some time to journal about this experience. Did the scene play out like you expected? What surprised you? What would you do differently next time?

In your community: One way to love your community is to make it a lovely place to live. Walk around your neighborhood and do something to make your neighbor's life less stressful. Take 20 minutes to pick up trash, rake leaves, remove snow, spread mulch, sweep steps or sidewalks. What impact does a lovely environment have on the whole community? How will your neighbor be affected by your help?

— MY IDEAS —

— READ MORE —

More about loving the stranger—1 John 4: 7-21
More about loving your neighbor—Matthew 22:36-40
More about how love never fails—1 Corinthians 13
More about loving like God—Colossians 3:12-17

Lesson 4: Belonging Together

— EXPLORE —

Isaiah 43:1-4, 10-13
Jeremiah 29:11-14; John 15:1-8;
1 John 5:1-5

— REFLECT —

Choose one of the 4 Scripture passages from the Explore section. Write down words and phrases from this passage that you connect with most.

Why did you choose this passage?

What does it say to you about belonging?

— CREATE —

My Faith Map
Make a map on pages 18–19. But not just any ordinary map. This map is all about you and your faith journey and the communities and individuals who have shaped you along the way.

— NEXT —

Ideas to Try This Week
At home: Share your Faith Map with your family. Point out the specific ways that your family has been influential on your faith journey. Then lead your family in creating a Family Faith Map. How does your family's faith journey compare with your own?

At school: Practice belonging this week by inviting two or three people to hang out with you and your friends. Invite people you don't typically spend time with and people you think would appreciate making some new friends. Why is "belonging together" important for someone's faith journey?

In your community: Find out what belonging means to someone in your church community. Spend some time talking with a member of your congregation about why belonging to your congregation is important to him or her and how it has made a difference in his or her life.

— MY IDEAS —

— READ MORE —

God knows you—Psalm 139:1-18
God's breath is life—Ezekiel 37:1-14
Connected through the Holy Spirit—Acts 2:14-21, 36-41

My Faith Map

Draw a map that follows your spiritual formation journey. Be sure to include your current location ("You are here!") and all the twists and turns (and dead ends) that it entails. What are the potholes, speed bumps, wrong turns, and one-way streets in your faith journey? And who has been with you along the way?

confirm

Lesson 5: The Faith of Jesus

– EXPLORE –

Nehemiah 9:1-13, 14-25, 26-38; Isaiah 9:1-7;
Micah 6:1-8; Luke 2:41-52

– REFLECT –

Lectio Divina (a.k.a. Divine Reading)

"Israel, listen! Our God is the LORD! Only the LORD! Love the LORD your God with all your heart, all your being, and all your strength. These words that I am commanding you today must always be on your minds. Recite them to your children. Talk about them when you are sitting around your house and when you are out and about, when you are lying down and when you are getting up. Tie them on your hand as a sign. They should be on your forehead as a symbol. Write them on your house's doorframes and on your city's gates." — Deuteronomy 6:4-9

What word or phrase did you focus on?

Why?

What did you notice in the last reading?

— CREATE —

Show and Tell
Follow the directions on page 22.

— NEXT —

Ideas to Try This Week
At home: Lead your family in the Reflect and Create activities. Invite them to read Deuteronomy 6:4-9 and capture a word or phrase. Then invite them to create an image or illustration on one half of a blank piece of paper. Have them swap with another family member and draw their image or illustration again.

At school: Find your history teacher and ask how learning about the past affects our present and our future. What is the significance of remembering our heritage? How does this shape our future? Take notes on what this teacher says and share them at your next confirmation class.

In your community: Research the history and heritage of your community. Visit the library, search online, and talk with your neighbors about what they remember about the history and heritage of your community. What difference does it make to know the history of the place you call home?

— MY IDEAS —

— READ MORE —

More about the Israelites' return to the land—Ezra and Nehemiah
More about prophets like Micah—Hosea and Amos

Show and Tell

In the frame below, create an image or illustration that captures the word or phrase you wrote down in the Reflect section.

Then, swap journals with someone else and re-create your image or illustration in their journal in the frame on the next page. This is a way to remember that our heritage is something we share with others rather than just keep to ourselves.

Don't forget to sign your artwork!

Lesson 6: The Early Church

— EXPLORE —

*Augustine, Gregory the Great,
Julian of Norwich, Francis of Assisi*

— REFLECT —

Dinner Time

Choose one person from the list below whom you would like to have dinner with. Where or what would you eat? What three questions would you ask him or her?

Augustine   Gregory the Great
Julian of Norwich   Francis of Assisi

Dear _____,

You're invited to dinner. We'll be eating _____.

Here are a few questions that I'd love to talk about with you:

1.

2.

3.

— CREATE —

Lights, Camera, Action!
Follow the directions on page 26.

— NEXT —

Ideas to Try This Week
At home: Go online and research more about the person from church history you selected in the Reflect section. Write down notes from what you learn and share them at the next confirmation class.

At school: Summarize today's lesson in five words. Share them with five different people at school.

In your community: Find some sidewalk chalk and recreate the church history timeline on the sidewalk in your community. Invite your neighbors to join you as you literally walk through the history of the church.

— MY IDEAS —

— READ MORE —

More about Christianity from Judaism to Constantine—
youtu.be/TG55ErfdaeY

Lights, Camera, Action!

Form groups of 3 or 4. Choose one of the people from the Reflect section. Spend 5 minutes researching more about his or her life. Then draw a quick storyboard of that life: How did this person's journey begin? What conflict did he encounter along the way? How did his life and work conclude?

Create a biopic with your group, acting out this person's life. (Bonus points if you use someone's phone to film the action!)

Character names and information:

How did their journey begin?

What conflict did they encounter along the way?

How did their life and work conclude?

Lesson 7: The Reformation

— E X P L O R E —

Martin Luther, Thomas Cranmer,
John Calvin, Jacob Arminius

— R E F L E C T —

Always Reforming

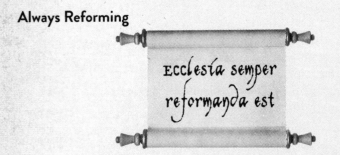

= "The church is always to be reformed." — Augustine

What does it mean that "the church is always to be reformed"?
Why, do you think, is this important?

— C R E A T E —

Three More Theses
Follow the directions on page 30.

— N E X T —

Ideas to Try This Week
At home: Choose someone from the list of people in the Explore section. Go online and look up even more information about him until you find something that you think your pastor or confirmation leader doesn't know about that person. Share that information with him or her at your next confirmation class.

At school: The Reformation reminds us that God works through ordinary and everyday people. Talk with your friends at school about the ways that God can work through you. Make a list of three things you can do to continue to bring the love of God to the people around you.

In your community: The Reformation reminds us that the church is reformed and always being reformed by God. Take a prayer walk around your neighborhood, reflecting on the ways God is continuing to move in your community. How is God inviting you to be a part of this movement?

— M Y   I D E A S —

— R E A D   M O R E —

More about the Protestant Reformation—youtu.be/1o8oIELbNxE.

Three More Theses

Martin Luther wrote 95 theses (statements) about how the church needed to reform (change).

Think about the church in our world today and come up with three more statements about how the church needs to change.

Write or draw them in the space on the next page.

Lesson 8: Wesley and the Methodists

— E X P L O R E —

John Wesley, Charles Wesley,
George Whitefield, Francis Asbury

— R E F L E C T —

But What Does It Mean?
Why is it important to learn about the founding of the
Methodist movement?

— CREATE —

A Methodist Timeline
Follow the directions on page 34.

— NEXT —

Ideas to Try This Week
At home: Write a short story about someone you learned about from the history of the Methodist church. Share your story with someone from your family.

At school: Hold your own "Holy Club" with your friends before or after school. What will you read? What will you talk about? What can your Holy Club do to make your school a better place?

In your community: Look up all the Methodist churches in your neighborhood. Send them a message online or stop by for a visit and ask them what it means to them to be a Methodist church.

— MY IDEAS —

— READ MORE —

More about the history of the Methodist movement—umc.org/who-we-are/history

A Methodist Timeline

Draw a picture or write a few words to fill out the timeline below. Use your creativity to bring the history of the Methodist Church to life on your page. Then answer the question at the bottom of the page. When your timeline and question are complete, share your student guide with a friend and walk each other through the timelines you created.

1703

John Wesley is born.

1729

John and Charles Wesley study to become priests and form the "Holy Club."

1738

John Wesley's heart is "strangely warmed" as he attends a prayer meeting on Aldersgate Street in London.

1739

George Whitefield asks John Wesley to try open-air preaching.

Thomas Coke and Francis Asbury travel to Baltimore to hold the first General Conference of the newly formed Methodist Episcopal Church.

1784

1771

John Wesley sends Francis Asbury to the first Methodist congregations in America.

1760

The Methodist movement spreads across the Atlantic.

Why is it important to learn about the founding of the Methodist movement today?

Lesson 9: The Growth of Methodism

— EXPLORE —

The United Methodist Church

— REFLECT —

One Thing

Complete the sentences below:

One thing I learned about Methodist history that I didn't know before is ...

One thing that surprised me most about our discussion is ...

One thing that I still want to know more about is ...

— C R E A T E —

A Snapshot of History
Follow the directions on page 38.

— N E X T —

Ideas to Try This Week
At home: Ask your parents or guardians why they choose to be a part of a Methodist church. Is it a part of your family heritage? Because they had friends at the church? Were there other factors that influenced this decision? Then ask them what they know about the history of the Methodist Church (and be sure to share a few things that you have learned).

At school: Find some friends from your confirmation class and issue a Church History Challenge. Go back and forth sharing things you remember about the history of the Methodist Church. Whoever can think of more things to share is the Church History Champion.

In your community: Walk around your church property and pay attention to the areas the church has grown and expanded into. Have there been any building renovations? A new parking lot? Fresh landscaping? Look for a cornerstone on the building that has a date of the church's construction. To learn even more, talk with a pastor at the church and have him or her tell you about the history and growth of your local Methodist church.

— M Y   I D E A S —

— R E A D   M O R E —

More about the formation of the United Methodist Church—umc.org/ who-we-are/formation-of-the-united-methodist-church

A Snapshot of History

Choose one of the moments you learned about from the
United Methodist history cards. In the space below, draw
a picture of how you imagine that moment taking place.
Then on the next page write your own historical fiction
short story, capturing the characters and emotions of the
events from that snapshot of United Methodist history.

Lesson 10: The Local Church

— EXPLORE —

Matthew 18

— REFLECT —

The Past Six Weeks
Read the passage below. Then reflect on the following questions and write 3 to 5 sentences in response.

"For where two or three are gathered in my name, I'm there with them." —Matthew 18:20

What have you learned about the story of the church over these past six weeks?

How does our local church fit into this story?

What does this mean to you?

— C R E A T E —

Time-Traveling Letters
Follow the directions on page 42.

— N E X T —

Ideas to Try This Week
At home: Talk with your parents or guardians at home about what church was like when they were kids. What has stayed the same? What has changed? And what do they think is coming next in the church?

At school: Find the teacher who has been at your school the longest and ask what he or she has learned from his or her time at the school. As you listen, how can you connect this teacher's experience at the school with someone's experience in the church?

In your community: Make some homemade greeting cards and write notes of encouragement to elderly or shut-in members of your church. It's important to connect with the whole church and not just the people who are the same age as you.

— M Y   I D E A S —

— R E A D   M O R E —

More about your local church—Visit your local library or history museum, or just talk with someone who's been there longer than you have.

Time-Traveling Letters

Write two fictional letters to your church. The first letter is
from the pastor of the church 100 years in the past. What does
he have to say to your church today? The second letter is from
the pastor of the church 100 years in the future. What does he
or she have to say to your church today?

confirm

Lesson 11: The Connection

— E X P L O R E —

Nehemiah 4

— R E F L E C T —

I Feel You, Nehemiah
Reflect on Nehemiah's story. Draw a picture of one scene that stands out in your mind. Then write 2 or 3 sentences describing why this scene stands out to you.

— CREATE —

Connect Them All
Follow the directions on page 46.

— NEXT —

Ideas to Try This Week
At home: Go online and research more about the structure of the United Methodist Church. Visit www.umc.org/who-we-are to learn more about how the UMC is organized. Search online to see how many UMC churches you can find near you.

At school: Talk to a teacher or principal at your school and ask them about how the school is structured and how all the parts are connected. How does it compare with the structure and connection of The United Methodist Church?

In your community: Find the three nearest United Methodist churches (aside from the one you attend). Contact them, either in person, over the phone, or via e-mail. Introduce yourself to the pastor and thank them for being a part of "the connection."

— MY IDEAS —

— READ MORE —

More about Nehemiah building the wall—Nehemiah 2–3
More about the United Methodist Church structure—
umc.org/who-we-are/constitutional-structure

Connect Them All

The United Methodist Church is often called "the connection," as each piece is connected with the others, providing a structure to "carry out our mission in unity and strength" (*Book of Discipline*, ¶701).

In order to show this interconnected structure, we are going to create a mind map in our Student Guides. A mind map is a drawing that uses shapes, lines, and words to show connections.

With a partner, create a mind map in *both* of your Student Guides. (Start in one Guide and copy in another or draw them at the same time.)

Look at the sample of a mind map provided by your teacher.

Turn your Student Guide sideways, and begin creating your mind map on the the next page. Draw in the center a shape with the letters *UMC* in it.

Around the page, add shapes a with the seven components of the UMC:

> General Conference, Annual Conference, Districts, Local Churches, Bishops, Pastors, *Book of Discipline*.

Use lines and words to connect the seven components with the center and one another. Make as many connections as you can!

Be creative! Add sketches, doodles, and colors to give your mind map flair.

Along the way ask your confirmation leader more about the various pieces of the UMC and how they are all a part of "The Connection."

Lesson 12: Simple Worship

— E X P L O R E —

John 4:1-24

— R E F L E C T —

Defining Worship

Draw or write your definition of the word *worship*. Use your creativity and include as many details as you can.

— C R E A T E —

A New Way to Worship
Follow the directions on page 50.

— N E X T —

Ideas to Try This Week
At home: In the Create section, you redesigned one part of a
worship service. Why not redesign the whole thing? Use your
creativity to come up with a complete worship service. Make
sure it includes all four movements (Entrance, Proclamation
and Response, Thanksgiving and Communion, Sending Forth).
Bring your ideas to the next confirmation class and show them
to your pastor or confirmation instructor.

At school: A United Methodist worship service has four intentional
movements. Chances are your typical school day does too. Track
the rhythms and movements of a day at school. What would
you call each one? What purpose do they serve? How do you
experience your day differently when you are aware of the "liturgy"
of your day? How do you experience worship on Sunday morning
differently when you are more aware of the order of service?

In your community: The final movement of the United Methodist
worship liturgy is Sending Forth, to enter the world and discover
and join the movement of God. Wake up early and take a walk
around your neighborhood. Where do you notice God at work?
Take the same walk again, this time in the evening. Where do you
notice God at work? What do you notice God calling you to do?

— M Y   I D E A S —

— R E A D   M O R E —

*More about worship—1 Chronicles 16:23-31; Psalms 29; 100; Romans 12:1-8;
1 Corinthians 11:17–12:30; 1 Peter 2:1-10*
More about worship in The United Methodist Church—worship.umc.org

A New Way to Worship

Read through the descriptions of the four movements of a
United Methodist worship service. Circle one movement (or
one or two specific pieces within that movement). Use the
blank space on the following page to design a new and creative
way to experience this in your church's worship service. Write,
draw, dream, and unleash your imagination as you explore a
new way to worship.

Entrance

From the moment we enter our worship space we are meant
to recognize that our interaction with God's presence has
already begun. This section includes: gathering, greeting, hymn,
prayers, praise.

Proclamation and Response

The Word is proclaimed through the scripture and sermon. The
church is invited to respond with our prayers, our offerings,
and our lives. This section includes: prayer of illumination,
Scripture, sermon, response, confession and pardon, offering.

Thanksgiving and Communion

Our response leads us to thanksgiving and occasionally the
celebration of Communion. This section includes: prayer of
thanksgiving, bread and cup, the Lord's Prayer, Communion.

Sending Forth

Just as we enter aware of God's presence, we are sent forth into
the world to join the movement of God and discover the ways
that our interaction with God's presence will always continue.
This section includes: hymn, benediction, going forth.

Lesson 13: Music and Lyrics

— E X P L O R E —

Colossians 3:8-16

— R E F L E C T —

A Song to Sing

Look through a hymnal, reading the lyrics to various hymns. Write your favorite lyrics in the space below. Be sure to include the title and hymn number so you know where to find it later.

— CREATE —

Move Over, Charles Wesley!
Follow the directions on page 54.

— NEXT —

Ideas to Try This Week
At home: Find a *United Methodist Hymnal* or go online and visit
hymnary.org/hymnal/UMH. Browse through the hymns and make
a list of your top five. Include your "old favorites" as well as new
discoveries. Be sure to read the lyrics closely as you make your
decisions. Then e-mail your top five hymns to your pastor or
confirmation leader and a friend form your confirmation class,
inviting them to send you their top five hymns.

At school: What is your school's fight song? Talk to the teachers and
administration and find out what it is. What is the melody? What
are the lyrics? What are they communicating about your school?

In your community: Pay attention to the music that you hear in
your community. What do you hear on the radio, car stereos, and
soundtracks to your favorite movies and TV shows? Make a list
of all the songs you hear over the course of one day. Then journal
about how these particular songs affect your experience of the day.
What songs would you want as a part of your soundtrack? Why?

— MY IDEAS —

— READ MORE —

More about Paul and Silas singing when they were in prison—Acts 16:16-34
More about one of the first Christian hymns—Colossians 1:15-20
More about singing in the Psalms—Psalms 95; 96; 98; 100

Move Over, Charles Wesley!

Hymns offer both an introduction to the theology of the church and space for our individual and communal connection with God. St. Augustine once said that when you sing you pray twice, the lyrics and the melody offering something unique and interconnected.

Write your own verses for the hymn "O for a Thousand Tongues to Sing." Each verse contains two 14-syllable lines. The last word of each line should rhyme. When you are finished, share your new verses with the rest of your confirmation class.

O for a Thousand Tongues to Sing   57

WORDS: ~~Charles Wesley, 1739~~ _____
                              your name here

Lesson 14: Remembrance

— EXPLORE —

Matthew 26:17-30; Mark 14:12-26; Luke 22:17-20

— REFLECT —

Celebrating Grace

Reflect on a time your church celebrated Communion.
Write 2 or 3 sentences describing this experience, what you
noticed, and how you felt.

What does taking Communion mean to you?

— CREATE —

You're Invited!
Follow the directions on page 58 to make invitations.

— NEXT —

Ideas to Try This Week
At home: Communion is about remembering. What objects or traditions do you have at home that help you remember? Are there photos on the wall? Family traditions that you do? Explore some of the ways you and your family remember the experiences you've had and the love that you share.

At school: Gather your friends from confirmation class and eat lunch together. As you share your meal together, talk more about the things you remember from this lesson about Communion. How does it feel to talk about this sacred meal during an ordinary one?

In your community: Talk with your family and then invite your neighbors over for a meal. The only purpose of this invitation is to get to know them better. Pay attention to where you notice God in the midst of the meal and your time together. How does this shared meal remind you of what you learned about Communion at church?

— MY IDEAS —

— READ MORE —

More about communion from the apostle Paul—1 Corinthians 11:23-26
More about communion from a story in the Gospel of John—John 6:22-59

You're Invited

Communion is an example of Jesus' invitational ministry, the good news of God's love for everyone. Design two greeting-card Communion invitations. The first card is an invitation to yourself. The second card is an invitation to someone else (yes, you will actually be giving it to someone).

On the front of each card draw an image that represents Communion. On the inside write an invitation to celebrate Communion with your church. Use a hymnal or Bible to help explain what Communion means to you.

Sketch your ideas here and on the next page before you make your greeting cards.

Lesson 15: Accepting Grace

— EXPLORE —

Acts 8:26-39

— REFLECT —

Making It Your Own

What is one thing you think Philip was thinking during the story you just read? Write it in a speech bubble below. What is one thing you think the Ethiopian official was thinking? Write it in the other speech bubble.

What do you think "being a Christian" means?

— CREATE —

Rising Grace
Follow the directions on pages 62–63.

— NEXT —

Ideas to Try This Week
At home: One way to remember God's grace is by remembering your baptism. Create small signs that say "Remember your baptism!" and place them around every source of water in your home.

At school: Baptism is all about grace, and grace is all about gratitude. Write nine thank-you notes to teachers and friends at school for things that you are grateful for. Then write a tenth thank-you note to God. Open your Bible to the story of the Ethiopian official (Acts 8) as a reminder of the connection between baptism, grace, and gratitude.

In your community: The story of Philip and the Ethiopian official reminds us that the grace we receive in baptism brings together communities that might otherwise remain separate. Where are there separations between people in your community (race, class, religion, etc.)? What can you do to help connect with others in the midst of a cultural separation? How do you think you will experience God in something like this?

— MY IDEAS —

— READ MORE —

More on the baptism of Jesus—John 1:29-34
More on the baptism of Cornelius the Gentile—Acts 10
More on Paul's theology of baptism—Romans 6:1-4; Galatians 3:26-27

Rising Grace

Baptism is all about grace. Baptism is "a gift of the Holy Spirit that united us to the body of Christ and leads us into a new way of life" (Mark Stamm, *Sacraments and Discipleship,* page 53).

Living a life of gratitude is one key way we respond to God's grace.

Look through the balloons on the floor—choose something you feel most grateful for and write a thank-you note to the person or persons you're grateful to for providing that.

Then, blow up one last balloon, and fold your note small enough that it can be put inside the balloon. Decorate your balloon in a way that expresses gratitude to the person.

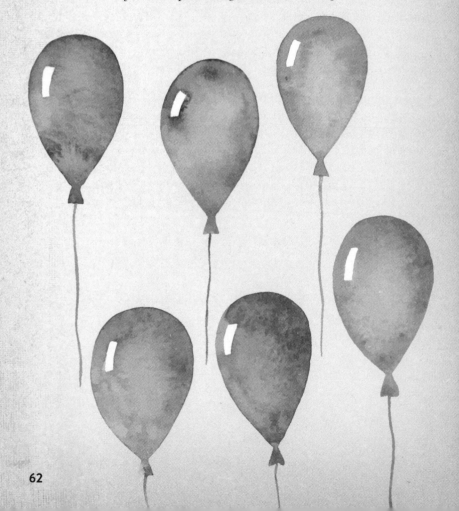

Write on the balloons on these pages some things that you are grateful to God for. How has God shown you grace?

Lesson 16: A Loving Church

— EXPLORE —

Mark 12:28-34

— REFLECT —

What About...?
What are some social issues in our community or world to which Christians should apply the house rules of "love God" and "love your neighbor"? Brainstorm as many as possible.

Choose three of these issues, and write a few sentences reflecting on the difference it would make if we were to apply love to that situation.

1.

2.

3.

— CREATE —

A Church Built on Love
Follow the directions on page 66.

— NEXT —

Ideas to Try This Week
At home: Talk with your family and create a list of all of your family rules. Then assign each rule to one of two categories: love God or love others. Do you have any family rules that don't fit in either category? Do you notice any family rules that are missing?

At school: Jesus tells us to love our neighbor. This week at school love your lunch neighbor. Sit at a table you would typically avoid and get to know someone who is different from you and your friends. What does this experience teach you about yourself? What does it teach you about God?

In your community: Jesus reminds us we love God when we love others. Find an organization in your community that you can volunteer with and help make a positive impact on the world around you (a food pantry, mentoring program, park cleanup, and so forth). How does this act of loving others impact the way you love God?

— MY IDEAS —

— READ MORE —

More about what it means to love others—Luke 10:25-37
More about what it means for the church to love others—Acts 2:41-47
More about what it means that God is love—1 John (the whole thing)

A Church Built on Love

What would it look like if the church were built on loving God and others? Think about the world we live in today, filled with war, violence, oppression, hate, division, racism, inequality, and more. Use your imagination to design a church built on love. Draw a picture of this church and add images and words to show how it could exist in the world. You may work with a partner if you choose.

LOVE

Lesson 17: So Now What?

— E X P L O R E —

Acts 11:19-30

— R E F L E C T —

The Work of the Church

Think back to the conversation you just had about the church in Antioch. Write your answers in the speech bubbles below.

What is one thing you heard your partner say that stood out to you?

How would you relate this story and the conversation you had to crises in our world today?

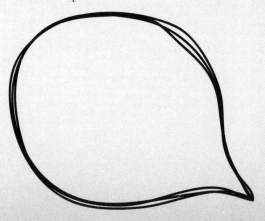

— CREATE —

Snapshots
Follow the directions on page 70.

— NEXT —

Ideas to Try This Week
At home: Go online and visit *umcor.org*. What is one way
that your family could partner with the United Methodist
Committee on Relief? Share what you learn with your family
and start a conversation about ways that you can be a missional
community that helps others in the midst of crisis.

At school: In confirmation class you asked what it would be like
if youth were in charge of the world. Talk with your friends at
lunch and ask what it would be like if youth were in charge
of the school. What would be different? What would stay the
same? How would you respond in an emergency or crisis? And
most importantly, what would be for lunch each day?

In your community: Talk with your pastor or confirmation leader
about things that your church is doing to help the community.
Volunteer with a group that already exists or discuss forming a new
group. What sort of things would you want to help with? Why?

— MY IDEAS —

— READ MORE —

More on the early church helping those in need—Acts 2:41-47
More on Paul collecting money for the church in Jerusalem—
2 Corinthians 8

Snapshots
What you do says a lot about who you are. Read the photo captions below and on the next page. Draw a snapshot of what you think the church should look like in each scenario.

A group of new Christians are in need of food and clothing (Acts 2:41-47).

There's a famine in Judea (Acts 11:19-30).

The church in Jerusalem needs help in their work with the poor (2 Corinthians 8).

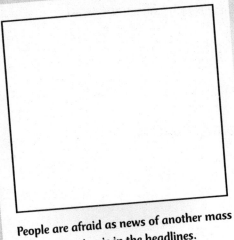

People are afraid as news of another mass shooting is in the headlines.

A severe hurricane hits the coast, leaving countless people displaced.

To find out more about how the UMC shows up in situations like this, visit *umcor.org*.

War breaks out in a foreign country, leaving thousands of families wandering as immigrants and without a safe place to call home.

71

Lesson 18: Faith and Trust

— EXPLORE —

Joshua 1:1-18

— REFLECT —

Faith Descriptions

In your own words, write a one- or two-sentence definition of *faith*, *trust*, and *belief*. How are their meanings similar? How are they different?

Faith

Trust

Belief

— C R E A T E —

Credo
Follow the directions on page 74.

— N E X T —

Ideas to Try This Week
At home: Go online and look up "Our Social Creed" on The United Methodist Church website (*umc.org/what-we-believe/our-social-creed*). Write down a list of words and phrases that you connect with most. Then write down a list of words and phrases that you don't agree with. Show both lists to your pastor or confirmation leader the next time you see them and ask them what they think about "Our Social Creed" and the parts they do and don't connect with.

At school: Talk to a coach or some students who are on a sports team. Ask them how trusting their teammates affects who they are and what they do. Then journal about their responses and your own understanding of trust in God and being a part of a faith community.

In your community: A credo isn't just something you believe with your head. You believe it with your hands and your feet. Take a prayer walk around your block, asking God to lead you to ways that your faith can come to life in the world around you. When you return home write down at least three ideas that you can try.

— M Y   I D E A S —

— R E A D   M O R E —

More about what the United Methodist Church believes—umc.org/what-we-believe

More about the United Methodist foundational documents—umc.org/what-we-believe/foundational-documents

Credo

Credo is the Latin word meaning "I believe." (*Creed, credo* — do you see the similarity?)

Write in the space below a paragraph or two that captures your credo, what you believe.

Then in the space on the next page draw a picture or cut out and glue down words and/or images from a magazine to reflect your credo.

Remember that this is *your* credo. It does not have to look or sound like anyone else's. But you are welcome to lean on the beliefs of others as you explore and develop your own.

Lesson 19: Experiencing God

– EXPLORE –

Psalm 34:1-10

Wesleyan Quadrilateral
Scripture is divinely inspired, and our primary revelation and resource for understanding God.

Tradition connects us to our a transcendent community of like-minded brothers and sisters who came before and will come after us.

Reason is our human ability to think and comprehend our experience and knowledge. Through the Holy Spirit, God gives us greater understanding of the truths of Scripture.

Experience moves us from just knowing about God to encountering God deeply and personally in the present.

– REFLECT –

Pillars of Your Faith
Which corner of the Wesleyan Quadrilateral do you find yourself leaning on most? Circle that word and then write a few sentences about why that pillar is important to you and your faith.

Scripture   *Tradition*

Reason   *Experience*

— CREATE —

An Illustrated Quadrilateral
Follow the directions on page 78.

— NEXT —

Ideas to Try This Week
At home: Traditions shape individuals and communities. Talk with your family about the traditions that you share. What traditions mean the most to each person? What impact do they have on the whole family? What traditions do you find confusing? What new traditions would you like to see your family embrace?

At school: Find your science teacher and tell them about "reason" as a part of the Wesleyan Quadrilateral. Talk with them about the ways reason helps us see the world as rich and filled with wonder. How does this conversation connect with your understanding of faith and spirituality?

In your community: Talk with two neighbors about their experience with the church and faith. What can you learn from their experience? What memories from your own life do their experiences bring to the surface?

— MY IDEAS —

— READ MORE —

*More about the Wesleyan Quadrilateral—*umc.org/what-we-believe/
wesleyan-quadrilateral

An Illustrated Quadrilateral
Read the prompts below and use your creativity to design your own illustrated quadrilateral in the spaces provided.

Scripture: Draw a story from the Bible that has affected you and your faith.

Reason: Draw a picture that comes to mind when you use your mind and think about God.

Tradition: Draw a picture of one of your favorite Christian traditions or a tradition from your church community.

Experience: Draw a picture of a time from your life that significantly affected your faith.

Lesson 20: The Bible— Not Just a History Book

– EXPLORE –

United Methodist Confession of Faith on the Bible

We believe the Holy Bible, Old and New Testaments, reveals the Word of God so far as it is necessary for our salvation. It is to be received through the Holy Spirit as the true rule and guide for faith and practice. Whatever is not revealed in or established by the Holy Scriptures is not to be made an article of faith nor is it to be taught as essential to salvation.

– REFLECT –

What Do You Say?

One thing I learned about the Bible today is . . .

One question I still have about the Bible is . . .

— CREATE —

Movie Poster
Follow the directions on page 82.

— NEXT —

Ideas to Try This Week
At home: Go online and search for images of old Bibles. What is the oldest one you can find? What is the story behind this ancient book?

At school: Canonization was the process of deciding which books should be in the Bible. How does your school choose which books they will use each year in class? Talk with your teachers, asking them how and why they decided to use the various books you are reading in class.

In your community: Visit 5 to 7 friends and families from your church, asking them their three favorite books from the Bible. Assemble the results of your community survey and share the results with your pastor or confirmation instructor.

— MY IDEAS —

— READ MORE —

More about the Bible and The United Methodist Church—umc.org/ what-we-believe/our-christian-roots-the-bible
More about what the Bible is and how it came to be—robbellcom. tumblr.com/post/66107373947/what-is-the-bible

Movie Poster

Now that you've learned more about the Bible, what it is and where it came from, design a movie poster that tells people about this ancient and sacred text.

What words and images will you use on your poster?

How will you design it to invite people to explore and experience the Bible?

Use your creativity and design your poster on the next page. When you are finished, share your design with someone in your class and ask about the poster he or she created.

Lesson 21: The Bible— A United Methodist View

— E X P L O R E —

John 14:26; Jeremiah 29:11

"The picture we have is of a creation at peace, abounding in harmony, in unity and fellowship, that this was God's intention for the entire universe because unity means peace, means prosperity, means fellowship, means justice, means wholeness, means compassion, love and joy conveyed in the virtually untranslatable Hebrew word 'Shalom.'"

—Archbishop Desmond Tutu

— R E F L E C T —

What Is It to You?
Answer the following questions in your own words:

Why should you read the Bible?	How should you read the Bible?

What is the connection between these two questions?

— CREATE —

Bible Blackout
Follow the directions on page 86.

— NEXT —

Ideas to Try This Week

At home: Read the Bible every day. Search online for "this week's lectionary text," click the link at the top of the page, and find the texts for this coming Sunday. Choose one to read each day this week. Journal your thoughts and reflections after you read each one.

At school: Bring your Bible to school with you. Read it when you have free moments. Pay attention to how carrying this book sparks different conversations with your friends and classmates.

In your community: One thing that makes the Bible unique is the way it feels different when read in different environments. Take your Bible and go on an adventure, reading the same passage (Psalm 46) in various locations. Find a quiet place under a tree. Stand next to a busy street. Sit in a space crowded with people. Find the tallest building you can access. How do these different environments impact the way you read the Bible?

— MY IDEAS —

— READ MORE —

More about the Bible and The United Methodist Church—umc.org/
what-we-believe/theological-guidelines-scripture

Bible Blackout

The Bible is a collection of ancient stories and poems and letters that still give meaning to our life and world today.

Create a blackout-style poem about what it means to be a person of faith in our world today. Cross out words, lines, and sections of the text on the next page to reveal the words and phrases that make up your poem.

Hint: begin by using a pencil to underline the words and phrases you want to include. This way you can write your poem and then black out the rest.

Example: Psalm 23

The LORD is my shepherd. I lack nothing.

He lets me rest in grassy meadows;

   he leads me to restful waters;

   he keeps me alive.

He guides me in proper paths

   for the sake of his good name.

Even when I walk through the darkest valley,

   I fear no danger because you are with me.

Your rod and your staff—they protect me.

You set a table for me right in front of my enemies.

You bathe my head in oil;

   my cup is so full it spills over!

Yes, goodness and faithful love

   will pursue me all the days of my life,

   and I will live in the LORD's house

   as long as I live.

Matthew 6:7-15

"When you pray, don't pour out a flood of empty words, as the Gentiles do. They think that by saying many words they'll be heard. Don't be like them, because your Father knows what you need before you ask. Pray like this:

Our Father who is in heaven,

uphold the holiness of your name.

Bring in your kingdom

so that your will is done on earth as it's done in heaven.

Give us the bread we need for today.

Forgive us for the ways we have wronged you,

just as we also forgive those who have wronged us.

And don't lead us into temptation,

but rescue us from the evil one.

"If you forgive others their sins, your heavenly Father will also forgive you. But if you don't forgive others, neither will your Father forgive your sins."

Lesson 22: The Holy Trinity

— EXPLORE —

Genesis 1:26; Matthew 28:19; John 10:30-36

— REFLECT —

Understanding God
Write a sentence to describe each of the following words:

Father/Creator

Son/Christ

Holy Spirit

God

— CREATE —

Three Logos in One
Follow the directions on page 90.

— NEXT —

Ideas to Try This Week
At home: A triangle is often used as a symbol for the Trinity. Look around your house and see how many triangles you can find. Challenge other family members to see how many they can find and compare your results.

At school: Sometimes the Trinity is compared to a dance with different people moving together in one divine activity. Pay attention to the relational "dance" that happens at school between students, teachers, and the building. How do these three components make up one school? How is this similar to and/or different from the Trinity?

In your community: Walk around your neighborhood and look for things that come in groups of three. Each time you see one, say the following prayer:

God almighty, creator of all things:
Show me your kingdom in this place.

Jesus Christ, light of the world:
Grant me your peace.

Holy Spirit, breath of life:
Strengthen and renew me
to do your work this day.

— MY IDEAS —

— READ MORE —

More about the Trinity and The United Methodist Church—
umc.org/what-we-believe/our-christian-roots-god

Three Logos in One

A logo is an image that captures an idea or an experience. Use the space provided to design three logos, one for each part of the Trinity. Then design a logo that combines parts of all three, turning your three logos into one.

Hint: a logo can be as simple or as complex as you want. Need some inspiration? Think about your favorite brands and products. Also, don't start with your final draft. Grab some blank paper and think out loud while you sketch your ideas! If you want, feel free to work with a partner.

Logo Design Tips
• Logos should be simple.
• Logos should tell a story.
• Logos should be memorable.

Lesson 23: Who Is God? (And Who God Isn't)

— EXPLORE —

Job 37:23-24; 38:1-38; 42:1-6

— REFLECT —

Reflections of Job
Describe a time when you experienced God at work in your life.

— C R E A T E —

Job's Prayer Journal
Follow the directions on page 94.

— N E X T —

Ideas to Try This Week
At home: Read the entire Book of Job. If possible, read it in a single sitting. Then go online and search for "the story of Job" to find out more about this ancient story. Spend some time journaling to reflect on what this story teaches you about God.

At school: Job's friends show up and fail to provide the comfort that he truly needs. Who do you know at school who is in need of comfort? What can you do to support them? Where is God in the midst of whatever they are going through?

In your community: Read Job 38. Then take a walk around your neighborhood with your eyes open to see God in the wonder of the created world. When you return home write your own version of Job 38 based on the things you saw on your walk.

— M Y   I D E A S —

— R E A D   M O R E —

More about God's faithfulness—Isaiah 43
More about God's love—1 John 4:7-21

Job's Prayer Journal

Reflect on the story of Job. What do you think he would have prayed to God throughout the various scenes of his life?

Use your imagination and write what you think Job would have prayed in each scene from his story.

1. Job is wealthy, healthy, and surrounded by his family.

2. Job loses his wealth and his family.

3. Job's health begins to fail.

4. Job's friends come to visit and blame him for his condition.

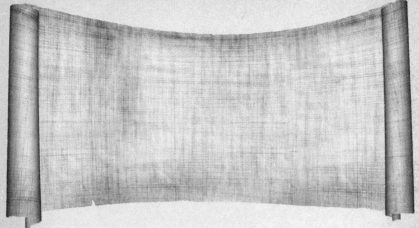

5. God appears to Job in a whirlwind.

6. Job's fortunes are restored.

Lesson 24: Prayer: Talking With God

— EXPLORE —

Adoration: Give God praise and honor.

Confession: Tell God what is heavy on your heart.

Thanksgiving: Let God know what you're grateful for.

Supplication: Pray for the needs of others.

— REFLECT —

Unfamiliar Versions
Write your own prayer using the ACTS model.

— CREATE —

In My Own Words
Follow the directions on page 98.

— NEXT —

Ideas to Try This Week
At home: Each night this week before you go to bed, write down a prayer using the ACTS prayer structure. Then pray that prayer again when you wake up the next morning.

At school: Be extra observant this week at school. What do you notice happening around you? How can you pray for your friends, your classmates, and your teachers? Write down the names of the people you are praying for this week.

In your community: Find a local newspaper or local news website. Read about the things happening in your community. Say a prayer for each one.

— MY IDEAS —

— READ MORE —

More about God hearing our prayer—1 John 5:14-15
More about who we should pray for—Matthew 5:44
More about Psalms as prayer—Psalms 4; 17; 51; 63; 139
More about prayer from Jesus' parables—Luke 18:1-14

In My Own Words

Read the Lord's Prayer below. Then rewrite it in your own words in the space on the next page.

When you are finished, find the parts of your prayer that connect with each part of the ACTS prayer structure you learned about.

Pray like this:

Our Father who is in heaven,
   uphold the holiness of your name.
Bring in your kingdom
   so that your will is done on earth as it's done in heaven.

Give us the bread we need for today.
Forgive us for the ways we have wronged you,
   just as we also forgive those who have wronged us.

And don't lead us into temptation,
   but rescue us from the evil one.

(Matthew 6:9-13)

Lesson 25: Prayer: Listening to God

— EXPLORE —

1 Kings 19:3-13

— REFLECT —

Meditating on God

What is distracting you?

What parts of the Lord's Prayer did you connect with most? Why?

How did you notice God during this prayer experience?

— CREATE —

The Sound of Silence
Follow the directions on page 102.

— NEXT —

Ideas to Try This Week
At home: Each day this week, take a moment to pray before you fall asleep and right after you wake up. Don't focus on saying anything to God. Use this space to simply be still and listen to what God is saying to you.

At school: Be extra observant this week at school. What do you notice happening around you? How can you pray for your friends, your classmates, and your teachers? Write down the names of the people you are praying for this week.

In your community: Walk to a park and sit under a tree. Psalm 46:10 says, "Be still, and know that I am God" (NIV). Use this Scripture as an elimination prayer, removing the final word or phrase each time you pray:

Be still, and know that I am God.
Be still, and know that I am.
Be still, and know.
Be still.
Be.

— MY IDEAS —

— READ MORE —

More about knowing God's voice—John 10:27-28
More about finding God where you least expect—Genesis 28:10-22
More about creation declaring the glory of God—Psalm 19

The Sound of Silence

Think back to the story of Elijah in the cave (or open your Bible to 1 Kings 19:3-13 to refresh your memory). In the space below, write what you think Elijah would have written in his journal after this experience. On the next page, draw a picture of what you think Elijah's experience would have looked like. Be sure to capture Elijah's emotions on both pages.

Lesson 26: Looking Like God: The Imago Dei

– E X P L O R E –

Genesis 1:26-28; Genesis 2:7
Psalm 8:4-5; Romans 8:28-30

– R E F L E C T –

Your Name Here
Insert your name in the blanks below.

Then God said, "Let us make _____ in our image in our image to resemble us....
God created _____ in God's own image,
   in the divine image God created _____.

How did it feel to hear your name in the text?

What does this tell you about God?

Insert a friend's name in the blanks. How did it feel to read the text with your friend's name?

What difference does it make when we use our names in the text? What does this tell you about the image of God?

— CREATE —

A God Portrait
Follow the directions on page 106.

— NEXT —

Ideas to Try This Week
At home: You are a reflection of the image of God to the world around you. Use a dry-erase marker and find a mirror you use at home. Write the words "Imago Dei: I am made in the image of God" as a reminder to reflect God's image to the world around you every day.

At school: Find your school's old yearbooks. Look through one from each decade for as far back as you can find. How have the images of students at your school changed over the years? How have they remained the same? What do you notice about the image of God when you look at these photos?

In your community: Psalm 19 reminds us that the heavens declare the glory of God. (You should probably look it up and read it for yourself.) Take a walk outside and look up. What parts of nature do you notice? What does this show you about the image of God?

— MY IDEAS —

— READ MORE —

More about Jesus as the image of the invisible God—Colossians 1:15-20
More about the United Methodist Church's beliefs about the image of God—umc.org/what-we-believe/our-christian-roots-human-beings

A God Portrait

Look through magazines and select one image that reflects your image of God. Cut it out and glue it in the picture frame.

Then write 3 to 5 sentences describing why this image reflects your image of God. What characteristics of God does this image communicate? Why did you choose this image? What does this image of God mean to you?

Imago Dei / *ih-MAH-goh DAY* / noun / Latin

A theological term, applied uniquely to humans, which denotes the symbolical relation between God and humanity.

Lesson 27: Hitting the Mark: Sin and Grace

— EXPLORE —

Genesis 2:15–3:13;
Romans 3:23; Romans 7:15-24

— REFLECT —

Sin and Grace: Defined

In your own words, write a one-sentence definition each of the following words. Then answer the questions in the space below.

sin / *SIN* / noun / Latin

grace / *GRAYS* / noun / Latin

What is the relationship between sin and grace?

When was a time that you experienced grace?

— CREATE —

Grace Over Sin
Follow the directions on page 110.

— NEXT —

Ideas to Try This Week
At home: Each morning this week, read Romans 3:23-25 when you wake up. What does it feel like to be reminded of God's grace covering our sin every day?

At school: Who are the people who get on your nerves at school? Make it your goal to extend grace to them this week (and beyond!). What does extending grace to others teach you about the way God extends grace to you?

In your community: Look through your local newspaper. (In case you've never seen one, a newspaper is like an old-fashioned paper website.) Look for headlines and stories about hurt, pain, brokenness, and sin. Use a marker to write the word *grace* over each of theses stories. What would it look like for grace to cover sin in your community?

— MY IDEAS —

— READ MORE —

More about The United Methodist Church's understanding of sin—
umc.org/what-we-believe/we-confess-our-sin

Grace Over Sin

Create a "grace-over-sin" piece of artwork across the space on this page and the next page.

First, select a light-colored marker and write the word *sin* 10–20 times, filling the space.

Then, select a dark-colored marker and repeatedly write the word *grace,* filling the space and covering the "sin."

Be creative in the ways you write the words and the designs you make.

When you are done, share your piece of art with someone else from your class.

Lesson 28: Two Natures, One Man: Who Is Jesus?

— EXPLORE —

Mark 5:1-17; 8:23-24; Luke 2:41-52; 5:27-32;
John 1:1-18; 14:8-11

— REFLECT —

Jesus in Context
Answer the following questions in your own words:

What does it mean to be fully human?

What does it mean to be fully divine?

What does it mean to be fully human and fully divine?

— CREATE —

An Illustrated Paradox
Follow the directions on page 114.

— NEXT —

Ideas to Try This Week
At home: Share a summary of what you learned about Jesus being fully human and fully divine with your family. Ask them why they think this is important. For an extra challenge, invite them to draw their own illustrated paradoxes.

At school: The poet Walt Whitman once wrote, "I contain multitudes." What are the "multitudes" that you contain at school? How many different roles do you play in a given day? Pay attention to each one, inviting yourself to be fully you every time.

In your community: Take a walk at sunset. Pay attention to the world around you to notice moments that are fully human (garbage on the side of the street, traffic and noise) and fully divine (the wind blowing through the leaves, the sunset on the horizon). What does it mean to you to live in a world where you can experience both the human and the divine?

— MY IDEAS —

— READ MORE —

More about The United Methodist Church's understanding of Jesus as fully human and fully divine—umc.org/what-we-believe/our-christian-roots-jesus

An Illustrated Paradox

Use your creativity and draw a picture to illustrate each paradox. Then write 3 or 5 sentences on why it is important that Jesus is both fully human and fully divine.

Fully wet and fully dry.

Fully hot and fully cold.

Fully up and fully down.

Fully human and fully divine.

In your opinion, why is it important that Jesus is both fully human and fully divine?

Lesson 29: What Is Salvation?

— EXPLORE —

Luke 7:36-50; Luke 19:1-10; John 3:16-21;
John 4:7-30, 39-42; John 10:7-10; Ephesians 2:1, 4-10

— REFLECT —

Grace, Grace, Grace
Answer the following questions about grace:

• How would you explain grace to someone who had never heard of it before?

• What does it mean to you that God has been gracious toward you?

— CREATE —

Was, Is, and Will Be

Follow the directions on page 118.

— NEXT —

Ideas to Try This Week

At home: Go online and search for "salvation stories" or ask people to share their salvation stories on social media. How do these stories resonate with your own?

At school: Take a sticky note for each textbook you use at school and write, "Was saved, is saved, and will be saved" on each one. Place one of these sticky notes on the inside front cover of each book to remind you about God's salvation throughout the day.

In your community: We see God's salvation rooted in the Exodus narrative with God liberating God's people from oppression. When you look at your community and our world, where do you see oppression? Journal about what it would look like for God's salvation to offer liberation from this oppression. What can you do this week in your community to be a part of this liberation?

— MY IDEAS —

— READ MORE —

More about a conversation Jesus had about salvation—John 3:1-21

More about salvation in the early church—Acts 2:37-47

More about The United Methodist Church's understanding of salvation— umc.org/what-we-believe/we-are-saved

Was, Is, and Will Be

Answer the following questions in your own words:

What is salvation?

What does it mean to be saved?

Salvation is not something that happens once. Salvation continues to happen in our lives both now and in the future. Using words or images, create a snapshot describing how you were saved, how you are being saved today, and how you anticipate God continuing to save you in the future.

"I was saved."

"I am being saved."

"I will be saved."

Lesson 30: Divine Helper: The Holy Spirit as Guide

— EXPLORE —

John 14:15-17, 25-27; Acts 1:8; Acts 2:1-4; Acts 8:29-31; Romans 8:26-27; 1 Corinthians 2:12-13; 1 Corinthians 12:4-7

— REFLECT —

I Ain't Afraid of No Ghost!

How have you experienced the Holy Spirit in your life?

— CREATE —

Who You Gonna Call?
Follow the directions on page 122.

— NEXT —

Ideas to Try This Week
At home: The Greek and Hebrew words for "Spirit" also mean
"breath." Find a quiet space where you won't be disturbed.
Set a timer for five minutes (or longer) and just breathe. Don't
focus on your thoughts but just focus on each breath in and
out. What does this experience show you about the Holy Spirit?

At school: The Holy Spirit is our comforter and encourager.
Choose three people at school and do something intentional
this week to help comfort and encourage them. How do you
feel the Holy Spirit with you and within you in these moments?

In your community: The Greek and Hebrew words for "Spirit"
also mean "wind." Take a walk outside and pay attention to the
air against your skin. Is it soothing? Refreshing? How does this
natural sensation connect you with the Holy Spirit? Each time
you feel the breeze whisper a prayer of "Thank you."

— MY IDEAS —

— READ MORE —

More about Jesus and the Holy Spirit—Luke 4:1-30
More about the first Christians and the Holy Spirit—Acts 2:1-47
*More about The United Methodist Church's understanding the Holy
Spirit—umc.org/what-we-believe/our-christian-roots-the-holy-spirit*

Who You Gonna Call?

The Holy Spirit is always with us, as close as our very breath. Jesus reminds us that no matter what you are doing or where you find yourself, the Holy Spirit is our comforter.

Choose one of the scenarios below or come up with one of your own. Write it in the box in the middle of the opposite page.

Then write two paragraphs: one from you to the Holy Spirit, asking for help in this situation, and the other from the Holy Spirit to you, providing comfort and encouragement in this situation.

Scenarios:

• You just found out you're moving to a new city.

• It's your first day at a new school.

• Your boyfriend or girlfriend just broke up with you.

• Your best friend just betrayed you.

• You got in a huge fight with your parents.

• You failed a big test.

Hint: Choose a situation that you might actually experience. This way the words you write to and from the Holy Spirit will be words you can lean on now and in the future.

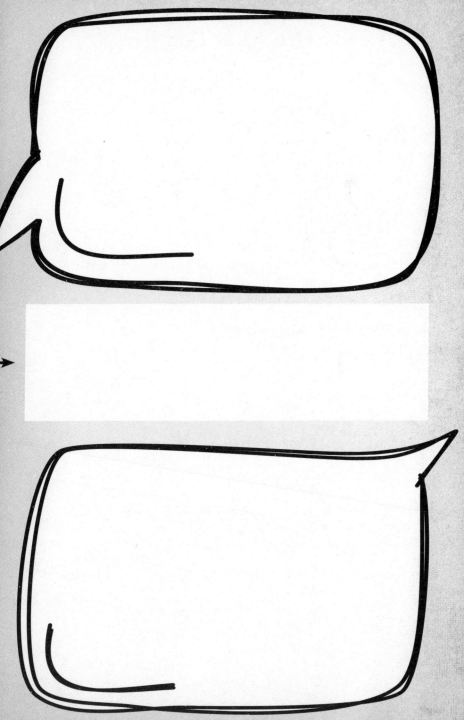

Lesson 31: What's Next: Life After Death

— E X P L O R E —

Matthew 25:31-46; Romans 8:35–9:1;
2 Peter 3:8-14; Revelation 21:1-8

— R E F L E C T —

The Next Place

"We don't live for ourselves and we don't die for ourselves. If we live, we live for the Lord, and if we die, we die for the Lord. Therefore, whether we live or die, we belong to God. This is why Christ died and lived: so that he might be Lord of both the dead and the living." (Romans 14:7-9)

What do you think happens after we die?

"Look! I'm creating a new heaven and a new earth:
    past events won't be remembered;
    they won't come to mind." (Isaiah 65:17)

In your own words, describe the "new heaven" and "new earth."

— CREATE —

Heaven: Coming Soon to an Earth Near You!
Follow the directions on page 126.

— NEXT —

Ideas to Try This Week
At home: Have a conversation with your family this week and ask them what they think happens when someone dies. Ask them what they think the "new heavens and the new earth" will be like and share with them some of the things you learned in your confirmation class.

At school: Write a letter to a friend at school, sharing with that person one thing you learned about heaven in your confirmation class. Ask your friend to share with you one thought or question he or she has about heaven or about life after death.

In your community: Rather than waiting around to go to heaven someday, we are invited to help bring heaven to earth each and every day. Talk to your pastor or other community leaders about ways that you can volunteer to help make the world around you a better place. Invite your family or your friends to spend a day volunteering together. What does this experience show you about the "new heavens and the new earth"?

— MY IDEAS —

— READ MORE —

More about *The United Methodist Church's understanding of what happens when we die*—umc.org/what-we-believe/what-happens-after-a-person-dies
More about *The United Methodist Church's understanding of heaven and the reign of God*—umc.org/what-we-believe/our-christian-roots-gods-reign

Heaven: Coming Soon to an Earth Near You!

Read the Scripture below. Then use your creativity to design a movie poster on the next page that brings these words to life.

(Be sure to include the title "Heaven: Coming Soon to an Earth Near You!" on your poster.)

When you are finished with your design, share it with someone from your class and tell them what it means to you.

"Then I saw a new heaven and a new earth, for the former heaven and the former earth had passed away, and the sea was no more. I saw the holy city, New Jerusalem, coming down out of heaven from God, made ready as a bride beautifully dressed for her husband. I heard a loud voice from the throne say, 'Look! God's dwelling is here with humankind. He will dwell with them, and they will be his peoples. God himself will be with them as their God. He will wipe away every tear from their eyes. Death will be no more. There will be no mourning, crying, or pain anymore, for the former things have passed away.' Then the one seated on the throne said, 'Look! I'm making all things new.' He also said, 'Write this down, for these words are trustworthy and true.'"(Revelation 21:1-5)

Lesson 32: From Whence We Came: The Creeds

— EXPLORE —

Hebrews 12:1-2

— REFLECT —

Documenting History
To know where we're going we have to know where we've been.

How does learning about the history of a movement teach you about where it is going?

What words or phrases from the creeds do you connect with most? Why?

— CREATE —

Credo
Follow the directions on page 130.

— NEXT —

Ideas to Try This Week
At home: Go online and post one of your credo statements on social media. Invite your friends online to do the same!

At school: Visit your school library and ask where you can learn more about the history of your school. What does learning about where your school has been teach you about where your school is today and where it is going in the future?

In your community: Who has lived in your neighborhood the longest? Visit them and ask how they have seen the neighborhood grow and evolve over time. What has remained the same? What has been lost along the way? And what new things do they notice emerging?

— MY IDEAS —

— READ MORE —

More about *The United Methodist Church's understanding of creeds—*
umc.org/what-we-believe/why-do-we-say-creeds

Credo

The word *creed* comes from the Latin word *credo,* meaning "I believe." Use the creeds you looked at today and everything you've learned so far in your confirmation class as inspiration to write a 1- to 2-sentence credo for each of the topics.

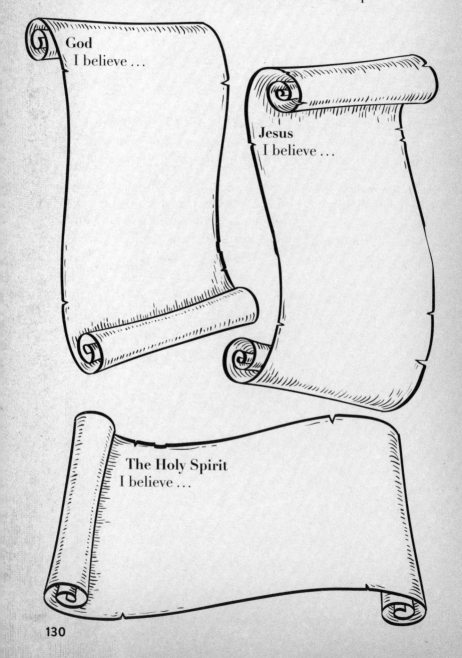

God
I believe ...

Jesus
I believe ...

The Holy Spirit
I believe ...

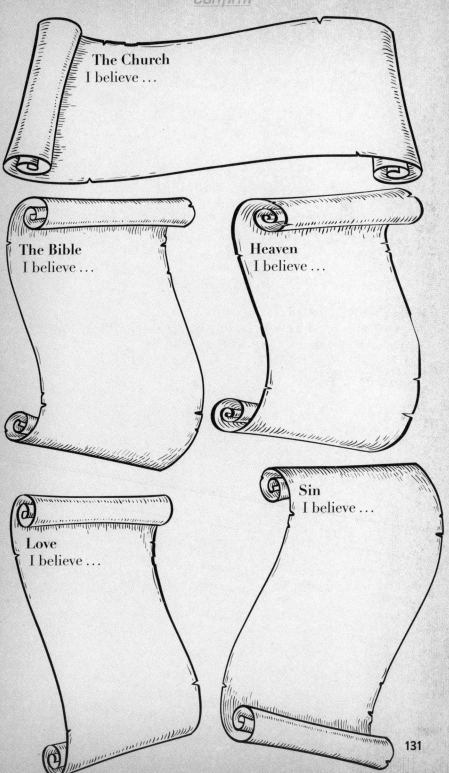

The Church
I believe …

The Bible
I believe …

Heaven
I believe …

Love
I believe …

Sin
I believe …

Lesson 33: A Faith to Decide

— EXPLORE —

Peter: Matthew 4:18-19; 14:22-33; 16:13-20; 17:1-9; 19:23-29; 26:31-46, 69-75; John 21:15-19

Thomas: Matthew 10:1-4; 19:23-29; John 11:4-16; 14:1-7; 20:24-28; Acts 1:12-14

John: Matthew 4:21-22; 17:1-9; 19:23-29; 26:36-46; Mark 10:35-45; John 19:25-27; 20:1-9; 21:1-8, 20-25

— REFLECT —

Documenting Emotions

How are you feeling about ending confirmation? Write down three emotions that you are feeling.

Which of the three disciples do you connect with most? Why?

— C R E A T E —

Dear Disciple
Follow the directions on page 134.

— N E X T —

Ideas to Try This Week
At home: Invite your family to read James 2:14-18 together. Have each member of your family write down one way that you can make more faithful decisions in your life.

At school: Every day this week pray for someone you do not get along with very well at school. Don't pray for yourself, but be intentional about praying for that person. At the end of the week, reflect on how you feel toward him or her.

In your community: Who makes the decisions that impact your community? Go online and research your city officials and council people. Reach out to the ones who represent your neighborhood and ask them about the process they use to make big and small decisions.

— M Y   I D E A S —

— R E A D   M O R E —

More about how Peter continued to follow Jesus—Acts 1-5; 10-12

Dear Disciple

Write a text dialogue between you and the disciple you selected in the Reflect section. Begin by telling him about a decision you have to make. Use your creativity to imagine how the disciple would respond. And then what do you say next? Use your imagination to bring this conversation to life, one text message at a time. (And don't forget to use emojis!)

Lesson 34: A Faith to Confirm

— EXPLORE —

Luke 19:1-10

— REFLECT —

Saying 'I Do'

Do you renounce the spiritual forces of wickedness, reject the evil powers of this world, and repent of your sin?

Do you accept the freedom and power God gives you to resist evil, injustice, and oppression in whatever forms they present themselves?

Do you confess Jesus Christ as your Savior, put your whole trust in his grace, and promise to serve him as your Lord, in union with the church which Christ has opened to people of all ages, nations, and races?

Write in the space below your thoughts and feelings about these questions: Which is the easiest for you to say "I do" to? Which is the most difficult for you? What do you feel God is calling you away from? What is God calling you toward?

— CREATE —

What Was He Thinking?
Follow the directions on page 138.

— NEXT —

Ideas to Try This Week
At home: Write an online message to someone in your family who is an example of what it means to follow Jesus. Thank that person for the example he or she sets, and ask him or her how you can be encouraged to continue following Jesus more and more in your daily life.

At school: Find a friend and commit to sending each other text messages throughout the day, encouraging each other to follow Jesus during the school day.

In your community: Write a letter (yes, the old-fashioned kind with a pen and paper) to someone from your church community whose faith inspires you. Tell that person how his or her faith has had an impact on yours.

— MY IDEAS —

— READ MORE —

More about following Jesus and the greatest commandment—
Mark 12:28-34

What Was He Thinking?

Take a moment to reflect on the story of Zacchaeus. Write or draw below what you think Zacchaeus was thinking and feeling at the beginning of the story.

Write or draw below what you think Zacchaeus was thinking and feeling at the end of the story.

After you finish both pages, share your creation with a friend and ask him or her how Zacchaeus might respond to the three professions of faith.

Lesson 35: A Faith to Live

— EXPLORE —

Deuteronomy 6:4-6; Matthew 22:36-40

— REFLECT —

Works for the World

Works of piety and works of mercy are means of grace. Circle all of the means of grace that you easily connect with. Maybe they are something you are passionate about or practices you do regularly.

In the next week, how could you continue to engage in the areas you've circled? Write some ideas here:

Works of Piety: Connecting With God	Works of Mercy: Caring for Others
Meditate on Scripture	Visit the sick
Pray	Visit prisoners
Fast	Feed the hungry
Worship	Give generously
Live healthy	Seek justice
Share your faith	End oppression
Participate in Communion	End discrimination
Study Scripture	Help the poor

Put a star beside the means of grace you would like to know more about or better understand.

Write down the name of someone in your church you have seen do that means of grace who might be able to tell you more about it.

— CREATE —

It's Off to Work We Go
Follow the directions on page 142.

— NEXT —

Ideas to Try This Week
At home: Choose one act of piety and one act of mercy that you want to intentionally practice this week at home. Make sure you do them both at least once each day.

At school: Talk with your friends about how you can care for others at school. How do works of mercy impact your faith? How do they impact the world around you?

In your community: Talk with your pastor and visit someone from your church who is in the hospital or unable to leave home. Talk with this person about what you have been learning in confirmation class. Ask about the things he or she learned in church at your age.

— MY IDEAS —

— READ MORE —

More about *The United Methodist Church's understanding of the means of grace*—umc.org/how-we-serve/the-wesleyan-means-of-grace
More about *striving for perfection—Philippians 3:12–4:1*

It's Off to Work We Go

Select one work of piety and one work of mercy from the Reflect section. Journal on this page about a time when you experienced one of the works. Draw on the facing page a picture about a time when you experienced the other work. When you are finished, find a partner and share what you have journaled and drawn.

Lesson 36: A Call to Follow

— E X P L O R E —

Saul—Acts 9:1-9, 17-22
Ananias—Acts 9:10-18

— R E F L E C T —

Tuning in God
Skills: When you begin to understand your skills and how to use them. List the things you are good at.

Excuses: A phase where you convince yourself you can't do something. List the reasons you have used to get out of using your skills.

Confirmation: God uses other people and experiences to motivate you to respond. Who has encouraged you to discover and use your skills? What skills and passions are they noticing in you?

Desire: When you realize that doing what you're good at brings you joy and God joy. How does it feel to use your skills to help someone else? How does the other person feel?

Opportunity: God provides the time and space to use your skills for God. List three specific ways you can use your skills and passions for God.

— C R E A T E —

Wanted: You
Follow the directions on page 146.

— N E X T —

Ideas to Try This Week
At home: Ask a family member whether he or she has ever felt led to do something out of the ordinary. Talk about how his or her decision affected others in the family. Ask whether he or she has ever considered what you might be led to do that is out of the ordinary.

At school: God's call to live for Christ is not something we add on to what we do. It is how we live our life every day. Consider the extracurricular activities you are already involved in related to your school (clubs, sports, ensembles, and so on). How might you be called to share God's love through those activities? Who in those groups might need to hear about God through you?

In your community: Saul (also called Paul) was called by God to serve the people outside his immediate circle. What do you think the world's greatest need is? How might God be calling you to meet that need outside of your immediate circle of church, home, and school?

— M Y   I D E A S —

— R E A D   M O R E —

More about God's call for your future—Jeremiah 29:11-14
More about God's call to Moses—Exodus 3:1-12
More about Peter's call to bring the good news to people outside his circle—Acts 10

Wanted: You

Write 3 short job descriptions. Look back to the words you wrote in the Reflect section for inspiration and ideas.

- In the first job description, describe the kind of person God is calling you to be.

- In the second one, describe something God is calling you to do right now.

- In the third one, describe something God is calling you to do in the future.

"God doesn't call the equipped.... God equips the called."

—Rick Yancey

"The place God calls you to is the place where your deep gladness and the world's deep hunger meet."

—Frederick Buechner

WHO GOD IS CALLING ME TO BE

WHAT GOD IS CALLING ME TO DO NOW

WHAT GOD IS CALLING ME TO DO IN THE FUTURE

Lesson 37: A Spirit to Find

— E X P L O R E —

Romans 12:4-8; Ephesians 4:11-13; 1 Corinthians 12:4-11

— R E F L E C T —

What Did I Get?

What are the top three spiritual gifts that you connected with?

How have you already seen God using these gifts in your life?

— CREATE —

Design-a-Ministry
Follow the directions on page 150.

— NEXT —

Ideas to Try This Week
At home: Find out the spiritual gifts of the others in your home. Compare the gifts God has given each person. Create a plan for how each of you could use your gifts at home to serve one another and make the family stronger.

At school: Ask a few of your friends what they think you are good at and compare their answers to the spiritual gifts that you have. What do your friends see about you that you don't see? How are you using your spiritual gifts as a witness to God's presence in your life?

In your community: Part of the importance of knowing your spiritual gifts is that it helps you use them to affect the world around you for the glory of God. Write down one way you can affect your neighborhood using each of your top three spiritual gifts. Try to do these actions during the week.

— MY IDEAS —

— READ MORE —

More about spiritual gifts in the Bible—1 Corinthians 12:1-31
More about spiritual gifts from the perspective of The United Methodist Church—umc.org/what-we-believe/spiritual-gifts

Design-a-Ministry

Use the open space on this page to write down ideas and make sketches of your design. The facing page will be used for the finished poster.

Work with a partner and brainstorm ideas for a ministry that you could do when you combine your spiritual gifts.

Who would you help? What would you do? How would you bring love and justice to the world around you?

Come up with a name for this new ministry and design a poster describing what it is and what you do.

When you're finished, show your new ministry idea to your confirmation leader. Talk about ministry areas at the church that you could connect with and use your gifts.

Lesson 38: A Story to Tell

— EXPLORE —

Luke 24:13-35

— REFLECT —

A Story to Tell

Circle one of the following questions. Take a few moments to reflect on it. Then write down your thoughts in the space below.

• When was a time or place when you felt your heart was "on fire" or "strangely warm"?

• When was a moment when your "eyes were opened" and you understood something that you hadn't before?

• What is a Scripture passage that was explained to you in such a way that it finally made sense?

• Who was a person who demonstrated to you what it means to live as a follower of Christ?

— CREATE —

I Believe
Follow the directions on page 154.

— NEXT —

Ideas to Try This Week
At home: Find a quiet place at home and read the letter you wrote at the beginning of your confirmation journey. How have you changed? Who do you want to tell? What will you say to them?

At school: Tell a friend at school about your confirmation journey. Invite him or her to come to the confirmation worship service and sit with your family.

In your community: God is with people even when they don't recognize it. Where do you see God in your community? How can you help others to recognize God is with them? What can you tell them about your confirmation journey as an example?

— MY IDEAS —

— READ MORE —

More about sharing your faith—Matthew 28:16-20; Acts 8:26-40
More about the faith stories of others in The United Methodist Church—
umc.org/what-we-believe/faith-stories

I Believe

Use this page to outline ideas and thoughts about what you believe. Then write on the next page your own statement of faith, describing what you believe and why you believe it.

Your statement should include but not be limited to the following:

• God, Jesus, and the Holy Spirit

• Following Christ

• The role of the Bible in your life

• Christian community and the church

• What it means to commit your life to Christ

Lesson 39: A Journey to Continue

— EXPLORE —

Ephesians 2:14-22

— REFLECT —

Affirmation Exploration
What affirmation surprised you most? Why?

How do these affirmations make you feel about being a part of a Christian community?

How does giving others affirmations make you feel?

How does this activity strengthen your faith?

— CREATE —

Looking Back, Looking Forward
Follow the directions on page 158.

— NEXT —

Ideas to Try This Week
At home: Find a quiet space in your house and read through the affirmation letters you received. What do these letters make you think and feel? How do they affect your decision to be a part of a faith community?

At school: Give a positive affirmation to someone who looks like he or she needs it. Don't make it about appearance or performance, but about his or her character or how he or she treated someone else.

In your community: There is plenty of negativity in the world around us, but Christians are a people of hope and love. Take a few minutes to look around your community this week and see the positive things happening. Be sure to point this out to others either in conversation or through social media. Be a voice of hope and love to your neighbors.

— MY IDEAS —

— READ MORE —

More about having your faith affirmed—Ephesians 3:14-21
More about remembering that you are never alone in your faith—
Hebrews 12:1-3

Looking Back, Looking Forward

To know where you're going, you have to know where you have been.

Fill the space below with words and images that describe who you were when you began your confirmation journey.

To know where you are, you have to know where you are going.

Fill the space below with words and images that describe where you think your journey will take you next.